Curious George and the Science Fair

Written by Francie Alexander

Houghton Mifflin Harcourt
Boston   New York

George is a curious monkey
These kids are curious too.
They are getting ready for
the science fair.

What is Jen making?

Jen is making a mobile
about the planets.

What is Will doing?

Will is growing a plant.

What is Ava doing?

Ava is drawing the life cycle of a butterfly.

What is Curious George making?

Oh, no! He is making a mess.

What will he do?

He will get help.

He will try again.

What did George do?

He showed what will sink and what will float.

Hooray for Science Fair Day!